SILVER CITY

OLIVIA CUARTERO-BRIGGS

LUCA MERLI

DAVE SHARPE

C I T Y

OLIVIA CUARTERO-BRIGGS writer

LUCA MERLI artist & colorist

DAVE SHARPE letterer

ROBERTA INGRANATA w/ **BRYAN VALENZA** front & original covers

ENTACUS (CASEY WULLNER), INGRID GALA & **DAVID LOPEZ** variant covers

DAVE SHARPE logo designer

CHARLES PRITCHETT issue #1 backmatter designer

COREY BREEN book designer

CHRISTINA HARRINGTON editor

created by **OLIVIA CUARTERO-BRIGGS**

AFTERSHOCK™

MIKE MARTS - Editor-in-Chief • **JOE PRUETT** - Publisher/CCO • **LEE KRAMER** - President • **JON KRAMER** - Chief Executive Officer
STEVE ROTTERDAM - SVP, Sales & Marketing • **DAN SHIRES** - VP, Film & Television UK • **CHRISTINA HARRINGTON** - Managing Editor
MARC HAMMOND - Sr. Retail Sales Development Manager • **RUTHANN THOMPSON** - Sr. Retailer Relations Manager
KATHERINE JAMISON - Marketing Manager • **KELLY DIODATI** - Ambassador Outreach Manager • **BLAKE STOCKER** - VP, Finance
AARON MARION - Publicist • **LISA MOODY** - Finance • **RYAN CARROLL** - Director, Comics/Film/TV Liaison • **JAWAD QURESHI** - Technology Advisor/Strategist
RACHEL PINNELAS - Social Community Manager • **CHARLES PRITCHETT** - Design & Production Manager • **COREY BREEN** - Collections Production
TEODORO LEO - Associate Editor • **STEPHANIE CASEBIER** & **SARAH PRUETT** - Publishing Assistants

AfterShock Logo Design by **COMICRAFT**
Publicity: contact **AARON MARION** (aaron@publichausagency.com) & **RYAN CROY** (ryan@publichausagency.com) at **PUBLICHAUS**
Special thanks to: **ATOM! FREEMAN, IRA KURGAN, MARINE KSADZHIKYAN, KEITH MANZELLA, ANTHONY MILITANO, ANTONIA LIANOS, STEPHAN NILSON** & **ED ZAREMBA**

AFTERSHOCKCOMICS.COM Follow us on social media

INTRODUCTION

Almost fifteen years ago now, I had the most vivid dream of my life: I woke up in a dark room, surrounded by people I'd never met, in a strange, overcrowded metropolis I'd never seen before. I had died somehow, and now, not only was my life over, but to survive in this God-awful place, I had to get an apartment, a job to support myself, perform monotonous public service, and, to add insult to injury, this was eternity.

When I woke up, I couldn't get the dream out of my head. All my life, I'd had *déjà vu*, that weird sensation of knowing someone I'd only just met, and had been fascinated with the afterlife. Suddenly, this strange vision and the story it presented felt like the chance to explore all those phenomenas, and more. So, I spent the next decade and a half musing, mentally building a world and a mythos, simply put, about life and death. About how human souls continually pass through the afterlife to the land of the living, in form after form, with no recollection of the lives that came before — to live out another survival-based existence, in perpetual fear of our imminent demise. But what was so exciting to me about the idea that was taking shape in my head, was that life was never actually meant to be this way...

SILVER CITY is a fun, brooding, character-driven journey through an entirely new take on the hereafter that feels dark on the surface, but is buoyed by redemption; a testament to the strength of the human spirit, our ability to heal and to rise again, no matter the odds. Suspensefully peeling back layers of mythos and mystery, while redefining existence as we know it, SILVER CITY follows its badass heroine, Ru Corrado, as she goes from the misfit no one wanted to see, to the hero no one saw coming.

But SILVER CITY is more to me than just a dream-turned-artistic-reality. In a strange way, it's a message of hope. Just weeks before I began writing the comic, I had to put my dog, Snax, down. It was one of the most gut-wrenching experiences of my life. But the one thing that made it better was the ability to give him new life in this twisted, little story and the idea that even though it's a fictitious place — and not a very nice one at that — Snax's journey, his soul's mission, continues.

In the past year, between COVID and cancer, I lost both of my uncles, some family friends and my one surviving grandfather. I am not alone. Deaths have increased by twenty percent over the past two years all over the world. More than ever, we need to know that our lives and those of our loved ones are meaningful; that we have a greater purpose than to be here for a moment, then erased by an awful, suffocating virus. We need to know this isn't all there is, for any of us, and that, somehow, in some way, the ones we've lost can again be found in another plane, another time or in another life altogether.

Crafting these five books has been incredibly cathartic and healing for me. I sincerely hope that whoever you are, whatever you're dealing with, and whomever you've lost, that they do the same for you.

OLIVIA CUARTERO-BRIGGS
September 2021

1

THE ARRIVAL

FLIGHT 769
LOS ANGELES - HONOLULU
10:44AM

LAX

NOW BOARDING GROUP 4 ON FLIGHT 769 WITH SERVICE TO HONOLULU.

JUNIE? DID YOU HEAR THAT? WE'RE BOARDING SOON.

VALENTINE IS DONE, HERE BUT NOW THEY'RE GONE... ♪

...ROMEO AND JULIET ARE TOGETHER IN ETERNITY, ROMEO AND JULIET... ♪

NOW BOARDING GROUP 5...

THAT'S US, JUNIE.

HAWAII, HERE WE COME!

...FORTY-THOUSAND MEN AND WOMEN EVERY DAY, LIKE ROMEO AND JULIET... ♪

DUTY FREE

...FORTY-THOUSAND MEN AND WOMEN EVERY DAY, REDEFINE HAPPINESS... ♪

...ANOTHER FORTY THOUSAND COMING EVERYDAY, WE CAN BE LIKE THEY ARE... ♪

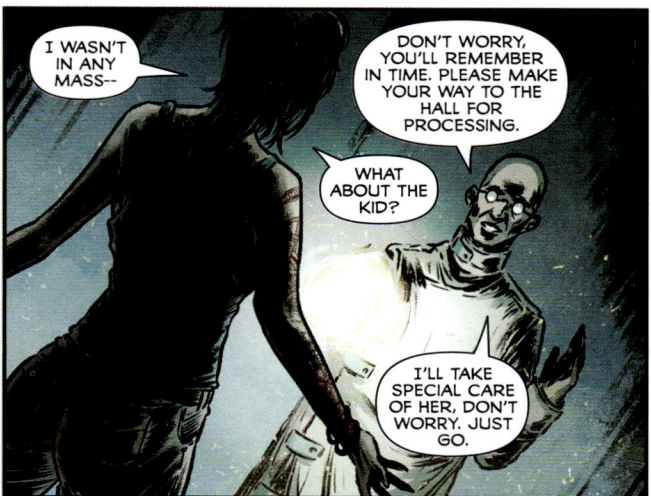

...THERE AREN'T ANY MORE ROOMS ON THAT FLOOR, SO I'M GOING TO TAKE YOU TO ANOTHER WING.
THIS WAY.

I SAW THE SUIT OF ARMOR OVER THE CITY, AND THAT BLUE EYE ON THE SWORD...WHAT DOES IT MEAN?

LOOK, I'M NOT SURE WHAT YOUR PROBLEM IS, BUT IT'S PRETTY CLEAR YOU DON'T WANT ME AROUND.

I DIDN'T SAY--

WHY DON'T YOU ASK VICKY, OVER THERE? HE'S GOT ALL THE ANSWERS.

YOU DIDN'T HAVE TO. I WAS A FOSTER KID FOR SIXTEEN YEARS, I KNOW THE LOOK.

BUT WE'RE ALL DEAD HERE, RIGHT? WHAT DO YOU HAVE TO LOSE BY GIVING ME A CHANCE?

FINE. BUT I SEE THE HINT OF AN EYE ROLL, AND WE'RE DONE.

SO, LONG BEFORE RECORDED HISTORY...

"...THERE WERE NO DIVISIONS BETWEEN THE WORLD OF THE LIVING AND THOSE OF THE DEAD.

"I MEAN, YOU COULD SEE THEM. THEY WERE RIGHT THERE.

"YOU COULD EVEN GO THROUGH THE LEVELS OF THE AFTERLIFE, FIND WHATEVER YOU WERE LOOKING FOR--

"--DEAD RELATIVES, FRIENDS AND WHATNOT--AND COME BACK. EASY PEASY."

"TILL THIS CREW CALLED THE *TIME KEEPERS* GOT SOME BRIGHT IDEAS.

"THEY WANTED TO TAKE OVER THE JOINT, HAVE SLAVES...YOU KNOW, WHATEVER THEY WANTED WITHOUT HAVING TO WORK FOR IT.

KA BOOM!

"THEY LEARNED PRETTY QUICK THE BEST WAY TO RULE IS THROUGH FEAR, AND WHAT DO PEOPLE FEAR MORE THAN *DEATH?*

"SO, THEY CREATED BOUNDARIES BETWEEN THE WORLD OF THE LIVING, AND THE EIGHT LEVELS OF THE AFTERLIFE. NOW FOLKS, DEAD OR ALIVE, COULDN'" VISIT FAMILY, WATCH OVER EACH OTHER, *NOTHING.*

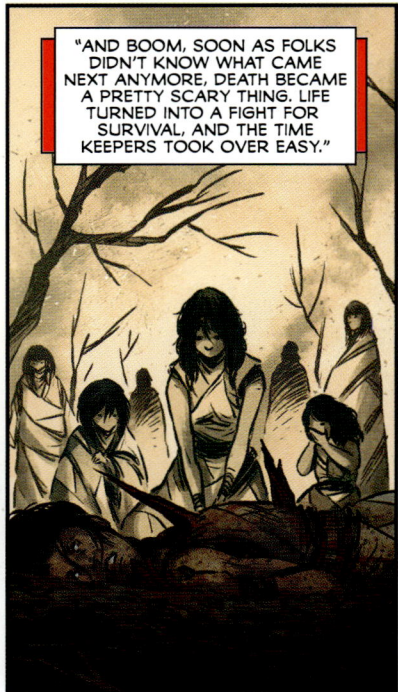

"AND BOOM, SOON AS FOLKS DIDN'T KNOW WHAT CAME NEXT ANYMORE, DEATH BECAME A PRETTY SCARY THING. LIFE TURNED INTO A FIGHT FOR SURVIVAL, AND THE TIME KEEPERS TOOK OVER EASY."

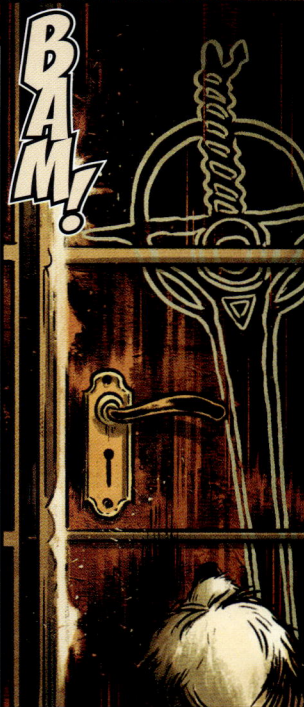

THE FOLLOWING DAY...
HEY, WHERE CAN I FIND ORIENTATION?
SECOND FLOOR. YOU'RE LATE.
ORIENTATUR
I JUST WANT TO GET BY!
DON'T BE SCARED, SWEETIE. COME ALONG WITH US.
I'M SUPPOSED TO BE AT ORIENTATION...
SUCH BEAUTIFUL SKIN YOU HAVE, DARLING.
GET AWAY FROM ME!
QUIET, CHILD--AND DO AS I SAY!
YOU'RE *HURTING* ME! STOP!
SILENCE! OR IT WILL ONLY GET WORSE FOR YOU!
HELP! HELP ME!
I SAID...
...SHUT UP! YOU'RE GOING TO STAY IN THERE THIS TIME UNTIL YOU LEARN YOUR PLACE!
NO, PLEASE! STOP! I'LL BE BETTER, I PROMISE, JUST...

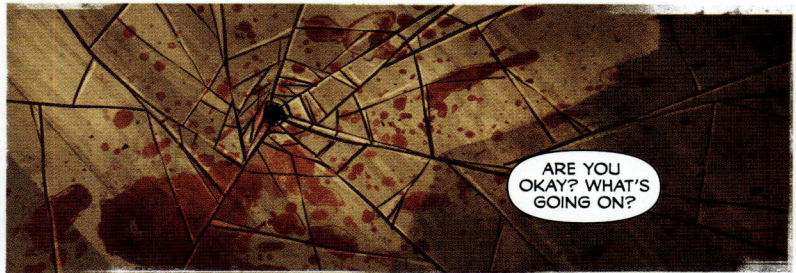

2

THE AWAKENING

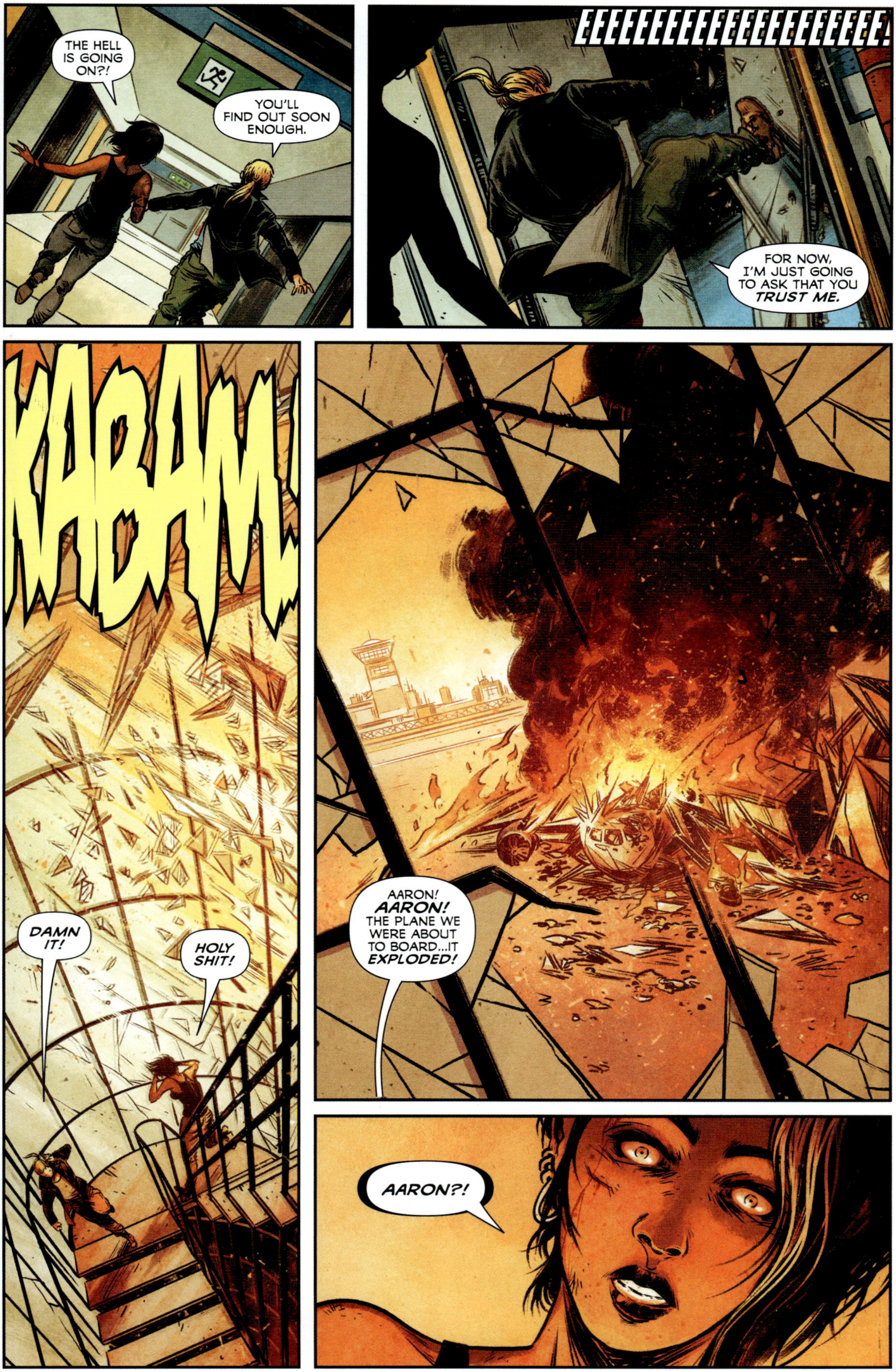
THE HELL IS GOING ON?!
YOU'LL FIND OUT SOON ENOUGH.
EEEEEEEEEEEEEEEEEEEEEE!
FOR NOW, I'M JUST GOING TO ASK THAT YOU TRUST ME.
KABAM!
DAMN IT!
HOLY SHIT!
AARON! AARON! THE PLANE WE WERE ABOUT TO BOARD...IT EXPLODED!
AARON?!

I TOLD YOU, FORGET IT. IT WAS AN ACCIDENT. IT WON'T HAPPEN AGAIN.

AND SECONDLY, DON'T PAINT *ME* AS THE MONSTER.

YOU'RE THE ONE DIDN'T WANT HER IN THE FIRST PLACE!

HEY, KID! WHERE'RE YOU GOING?

RU!

LIKE I TOLD YOU, I KNOW WHEN I'M NOT WANTED.

AND AFTER WHAT I'VE BEEN THROUGH, YOU'LL FORGIVE ME IF I DON'T WANT TO FEEL ANY SHITTIER.

HEY, WAIT UP A SEC, WOULD YA?

GOT SOMETHIN' I WANT TO SHOW YA...

MARY, MOTHER OF GOD...
...PRAY FOR US SINNERS NOW AND AT THE HOUR OF OUR...DEATH.
AMEN.
AH!
AH!
AH!
AH!
SFFFT

"...I TOLD YOU I KNEW THE *SILVER KNIGHT,* BUT I DIDN'T TELL YOU I WAS A *GUARDIAN* IN HIS ARMY."

"WE FOUGHT ALL THE WAY TO *NYDOR,* THE FINAL WORLD OF THE AFTERLIFE, WHEN I MET *RAVE TIERNEY,* THIS TIME DROPPER I SAVED FROM A HUNTER TRAP.

"WHEN HE FOUND OUT WHO WE WERE, HE BEGGED TO TAG ALONG. TO HELP, HE SAID.

"I'D BEEN WITH THE KNIGHT SINCE THE TANGEE DESERT. HE TRUSTED ME...MAYBE MORE THAN ANYONE ELSE. SO, WHEN I TOLD HIM RAVE DESERVED A SHOT, HE TOOK HIM ON."

"WE HAD JUST MADE IT TO *THE TREE OF RECURRIT*, THE GATEWAY TO THE LIVING WORLD.

"ALL WE HAD TO DO WAS GET THE KNIGHT THROUGH, AND ALL THE WORLDS WOULDA BEEN REUNITED...

"...BUT WE WAS *AMBUSHED.*

"I GOT DUPED, AND 'CAUSE OF ME, THE WHOLE MISSION WENT TITS UP."

"TURNS OUT, GOOD OL' RAVE WAS A TIME KEEPER RAT THAT SNITCHED ON OUR LOCATION.

"...MY EYES *ARE* GRAY."

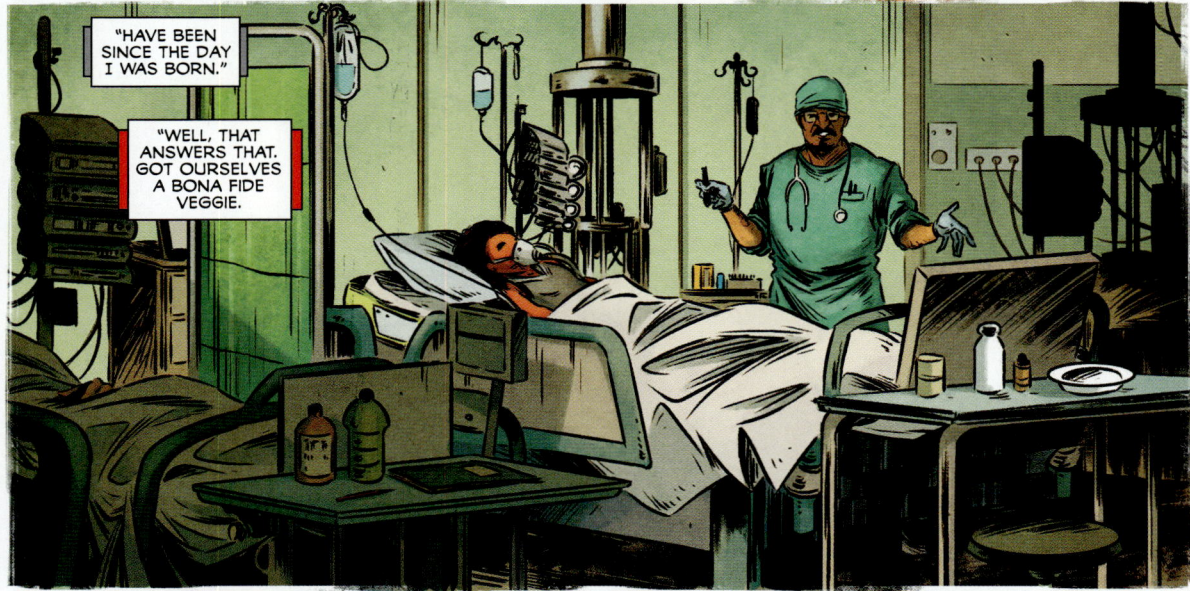

"HAVE BEEN SINCE THE DAY I WAS BORN."

"WELL, THAT ANSWERS THAT. GOT OURSELVES A BONA FIDE VEGGIE."

"MAYBE THAT'S WHY THOSE TIME KEEPER BROADS WERE TRYING TO GET THEIR HANDS ON HER."

WHAT ARE YOU TALKING ABOUT?

3

RETURNS

♪ YOU TELL ME THAT YOU LOVE ME BUT YOU'RE WAITIN' TO SEE, IF THE ONE WHO LEFT YOU CRYIN' GONNA GIVE YOU HIS KEY...

♪ ...YOU'RE SEXY BUT YOU GIVE YOUR LIES AWAY FOR FREE, SO...

♪ ...YOUR ANARCHY AIN'T ENOUGH FOR ME!

WHISKY A GOGO

TELLIN' YOUS, SHE HAD ONE OF THEM WRAP TOPS ON, AND IT JUST SLID RIGHT OFF HER!

FFSSSSFF

FRIEND MUSTA PULLED IT DOWN. GIRLS AIN'T DUMB ENOUGH TO HAVE THEIR BAPS FALLIN' OUT FOR THE WORLD TO SEE.

DUNNO. WE IS TALKIN' 'BOUT AMERICAN GIRLS.

OI, VICTOR. YOU ALL RIGHT, MATE?

JOHNNY LIVE

HEEEK!

BREATHE, VICTOR!

GET HIM TO HOSPITAL!

THEN THEY'LL KNOW WE'S BEEN DRUGGIN'!

WHO CARES?! HE'S DYING!

VICTOR!

BACK OFF! THERE'S NOTHING YOU CAN DO.

WHAT IN BLOODY HELL WAS THAT?!

THAT WAS YOU, WASN'T IT, RU? YOU MADE IT HAPPEN!

TAKE A CHILL PILL, VICKY...

NOT UNTIL SHE COPS TO IT! HOW'D YOU DO IT?

THE HELL ARE YOU?!

HEY! TAKE A WALK, I SAID!

I...I'VE HAD A HANDLE ON IT FOR YEARS. THERE'S SOMETHING ABOUT THIS PLACE--

AW, BLOODY HELL!

LEAVE IT TO ME TO GET SHACKED UP WITH SOME BARMY WITCH AND A PUBESCENT VEGGIE WHO'S GOT ARSEHOLES COMIN' OUT OF THE WOODWORK AFTER US!

WATCH IT, VICTOR. IT'S NOT HER FAULT.

"I HEARD SHE'S A WITCH..."

...KID IN HER LAST FOSTER HOME DIED IN SOME FREAK ACCIDENT, AND THE ONE BEFORE THAT, WHOLE HOUSE BURNED DOWN.

THERE ARE WAYS TO SEE IF SOMEONE'S REALLY A WITCH, YOU KNOW.

YOU SURE SHE CAN'T DROWN?

NOT IF SHE'S A WITCH.

DO IT AGAIN. *LONGER* THIS TIME.

"YOU EVER GONNA LEARN TO SHUT THAT YAP OF YOURS?"

OH, SORRY. DID I HURT THE WITCH'S FEELINGS? SHE OBLITERATED SOMEONE!

POOR SOD'S PROBABLY SO SMASHED UP THEY'LL HAVE TO TAKE HER TO THE WALL AS A MERCY KILLING.

RU...?

AAARRRRGH!

ALLS I'M SAYIN' IS, IF THE *TIME KEEPERS* ARE AFTER JUNIE, THAT GIFT OF YOURS MIGHT COME IN REAL HANDY GETTIN' HER BACK TO THE LAND OF THE LIVING...

YOU DON'T GET IT, MICK. IT'S *NOT* A *GIFT.*

BUT IF YOU JUST TAUGHT YOURSELF HOW TO HARNESS IT--

YOU'RE NOT GOING TO TALK ME INTO SOME WAX-ON-WAX-OFF TRAINING SHIT, OKAY?

DIDN'T YOU SAY THE UNIVERSITY HAD SOME SORT OF RETURNS PORTAL?

THAT'S WHAT THEY SAY.

PLACE IS CRAWLING WITH TIME KEEPERS, THOUGH.

AND IF SOMETHING HAPPENS TO JUNIE *DOWN HERE,* SHE'LL LOSE HER SHOT *UP THERE,* FOR SURE.

THEN WE'LL FIND A WAY TO SNEAK HER IN.

WE JUST HAVE TO FIGURE OUT WHERE THE RETURNS PORTAL IS WITHOUT LOOKING SUSPICIOUS.
THEN WE'LL COME BACK TONIGHT WITH JUNIE, WHEN THE COAST IS CLEAR, AND GET HER BACK WHERE SHE BELONGS.
YOU'RE REALLY PULLIN' FOR THAT VEGGIE, AIN'T YA?
YOU'RE PRETTY ADMIRABLE, YOU KNOW THAT, KID?
IF SOMEONE HAD BEEN PULLING FOR ME BACK WHEN, THINGS MIGHT HAVE TURNED OUT DIFFERENTLY.
RU?! OMIGOD!
STICKS! THERE YOU ARE!
THERE I AM?! WHERE HAVE YOU BEEN?
I TRIED YOUR TRACKING NUMBER, BUT THEY COULDN'T FIND YOU IN THE SYSTEM.
I TOLD YOU I'D FIND YOU!
I WAS SO WORRIED!
YOU WERE RIGHT, STICKS. I NEVER SHOULD HAVE TRUSTED AARON.

HE'S THE REASON I'M HERE.
NO! OH, HONEY...I AM *SO* SORRY!
A-HEM...
SORRY. STICKS, THIS IS MICK, MY...ROOMMATE. MICK, THIS IS *STICKS,* THE FRIEND I TOLD YOU WAS HERE WITH ME.
CHARMED.
LIKEWISE.
NOW, IF YOU'LL EXCUSE US.
WHERE ARE YOU GOING?
A GIRL WHO LANDED WITH ME; SHE'S *ALIVE.* WE HAVE TO GET HER TO THE RETURNS PORTAL, BUT...PEOPLE ARE AFTER HER--
RU! WHAT ARE YOU DOING?
WHAT? STICKS AND I HAVE KNOWN ONE ANOTHER SINCE WE WERE KIDS.
I KNOW WHERE THE RETURNS ROOM IS!
YOU DO?
BEEN LIVING HERE FOR THE PAST FEW WEEKS, HONEY. I KNOW THIS PLACE LIKE THE BACK OF MY CLAW.

WILL YOU PLEASE GET AN S.C. TRACKING NUMBER? I CAN'T LOSE YOU AGAIN.

I WILL, AS SOON AS JUNIE'S SAFE. I JUST CAN'T LET HER GET STUCK DOWN HERE FOREVER, LIKE WE ARE.

WAIT... HOW *DID* YOU GET HERE?

HOLD UP, HONEY.

IS THAT WHERE THE RETURNS PORTAL IS?

YEAH...BUT I'VE NEVER SEEN THE QUEEN'S FREAKIN' GUARD HERE BEFORE.

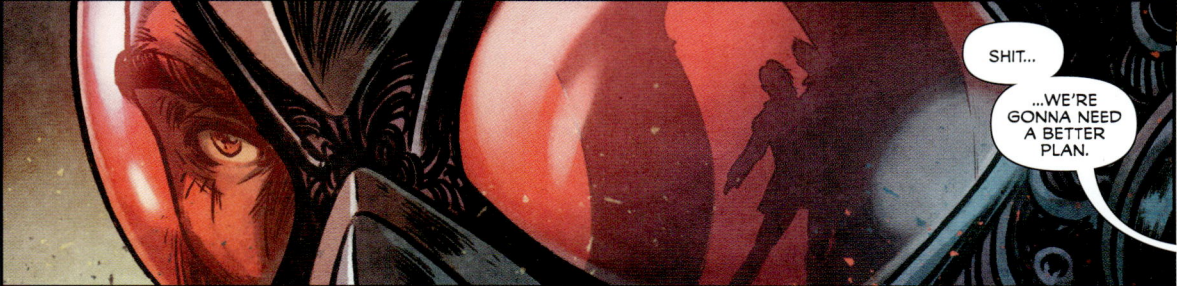

SHIT...

...WE'RE GONNA NEED A BETTER PLAN.

LATER THAT NIGHT...

HOW LONG THEY SAY WE NEED TO BE HERE FOR? I GOTTA TOP UP, BAD.

TILL THEY SEND SOMEONE TO RELIEVE US. NO ONE'S GETTIN BACK ANYMORE WITHOUT A DAMN GOOD REASON.

MORE TO GO AROUND THEN, I GUESS.

EXACTLY.

♪ YOUR LIFE IS AN OBSCENITY! ♫

THE HELL IS THAT?

♪ FILLED WITH GROSS INDECENCY! YOUR EYES LIGHT FIRES BUT STILL I SEE... ♫

♪ ...YOUR ANARCHY AIN'T ENOUGH FOR ME! ♫

4

BETRAYAL

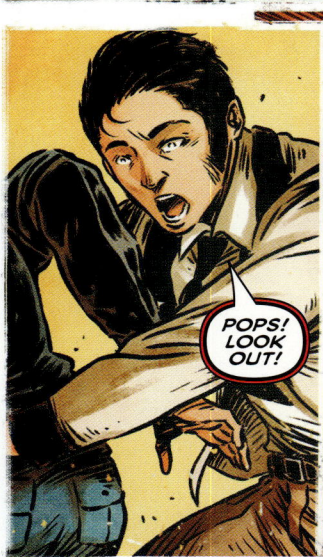

IF YOU CAN GET US BACK THERE, JUST BEFORE THE EXPLOSION, WE CAN KEEP JUNIE FROM GETTING HURT, AND ***NONE*** OF THIS WILL EVER HAPPEN.
AND IF I ***CAN'T?***
DON'T KNOW, KID. THIS MIGHT BE THE ONLY CHANCE JUNIE HAS LEFT.
WHAT DO I HAVE TO DO?
TRUST ME?
YOU KNOW BETTER THAN TO ASK ME THAT.
TAKE MY HANDS. THAT WAY, I CAN TAG ALONG.
NOW, YOU GOTTA CLEAR YOUR MIND OF EVERYTHING. LIKE, ***BLACK VOID*** EVERYTHING. GOT IT?

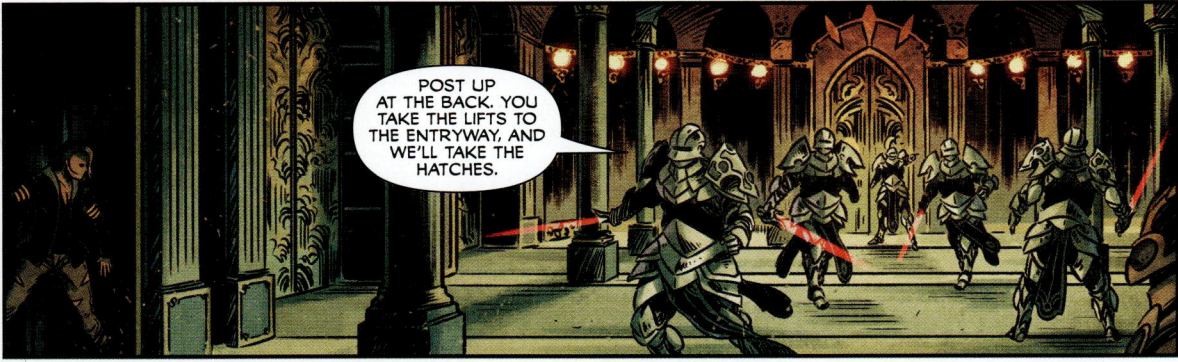

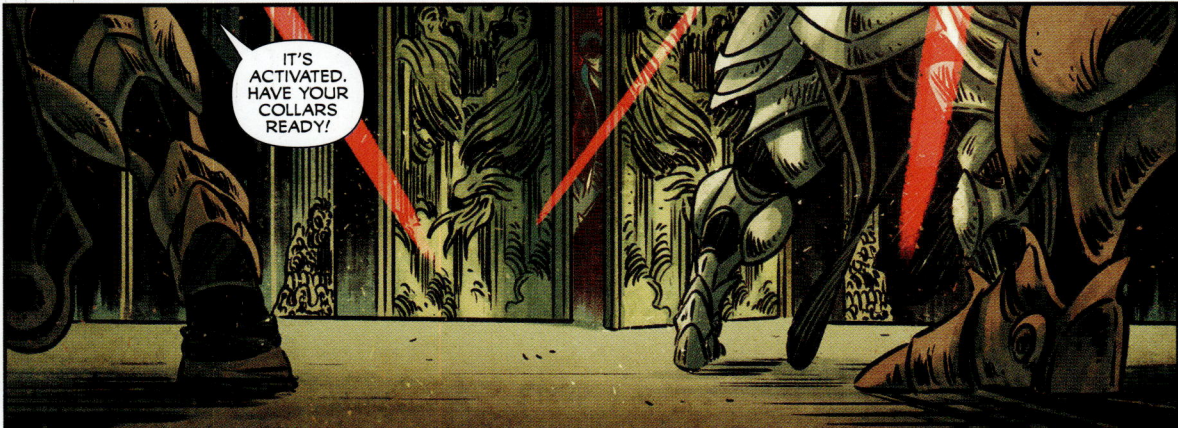

5

THE ANTECEDENTS

"I CAME INTO THE LIVING WORLD JUST LIKE EVERYBODY ELSE. BUT YOU WANT TO TALK ABOUT A *SPECIAL PURPOSE*?

"SEE, SOME PEOPLE ARE MADE TIME KEEPERS, BUT BABY, I WAS *BORN THIS WAY.* HA!

"AND I HAD A VERY IMPORTANT LIFE MISSION. PRETTY MUCH THE MOST IMPORTANT OF ALL. *TO BE YOUR FRIEND, RU.*

"TOOK THE TIME KEEPERS A BIT TO TRACK YOU DOWN, I'LL GIVE THE GUARDIANS THAT.

"BUT ONCE WE DID, YOU WERE PUTTY IN MY HANDS, GIRL. *BFFs.*

"AND I WAS SO DAMN GOOD! YOU THOUGHT WE WERE CHILLIN', BUT THE TRUTH IS, I WAS *TRACKING EVERYTHING...*"

"...STEERING YOU, INFLUENCING WHERE YOU WENT, WHAT YOU THOUGHT AND WHO YOU HUNG OUT WITH."

"THE ONLY ONE I OVERLOOKED WAS *AARON.* GUY SEEMED LIKE SUCH A WASTE OF GOOD LEATHER, I NEVER THOUGHT FOR A SECOND HE COULD BE A GUARDIAN."

STICKS, NO. I'M GOING TO BE FINE. JUST CALM DOWN, AND I'LL CALL YOU WHEN I LAND.

"PRETTY SURE HE GOT WISE TO ME FIRST. GUESS I WAS A LITTLE CLINGY..."

YOU MIGHT JUST BE MY SOULMATE.

SOMETHING TELLS ME YOU WON'T FEEL THAT WAY FOR LONG.

"THE GUARDIANS KNEW WE WERE CLOSING IN. SO, THEIR PLAN WAS TO TAKE YOU OUT, GET YOU BACK TO THE *AFTERLIFE* IN SOME MASS-CASUALTY EVENT SO WE'D LOSE TRACK OF YOU IN ARRIVALS."

"YOU WERE SUPPOSED TO *DIE* IN THAT AIRPLANE EXPLOSION, RU. I JUST GOT IN THE WAY."

KABAM!

AND IF THE SILVER KNIGHT GETS NEUTRALIZED, THE WHOLE MISSION'S KAPUT. ALL OF HUMANITY, DEAD OR ALIVE, WILL BE SLAVES TO FEAR *FOREVER.*

BUT MICK, I'M NOT THE SILVER KNIGHT.

I'M A MISFIT, A NOBODY. HAVE BEEN MY WHOLE LIFE.

BUT YOU *ARE.* EXPLAINS A LOT, ACTUALLY.

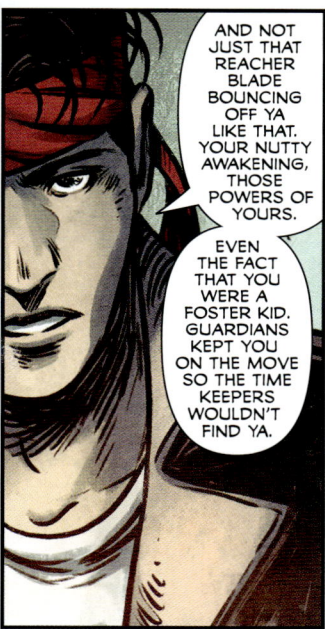

AND NOT JUST THAT REACHER BLADE BOUNCING OFF YA LIKE THAT. YOUR NUTTY AWAKENING, THOSE POWERS OF YOURS.

EVEN THE FACT THAT YOU WERE A FOSTER KID. GUARDIANS KEPT YOU ON THE MOVE SO THE TIME KEEPERS WOULDN'T FIND YA.

AND IF AARON WAS A GUARDIAN, THAT MEANS WHEN HE SHOT ME...

HE WAS ACTUALLY *PROTECTING* YOU. MAKIN' SURE YOU GOT DOWN HERE IN A CROWD SO YOU WOULDN'T BE DETECTED.

BUT YOU KNEW THE SILVER KNIGHT. HOW CAN *HE* AND *I* BE THE SAME PERSON?

WHEN WE WERE AMBUSHED AT THE TREE OF RECURRIT, THE GATEWAY TO THE LIVING WORLD... I TOLD YOU THE KNIGHT DISAPPEARED.

I THOUGHT MAYBE THEY NEUTRALIZED HIM THEN, BUT HE MUST HAVE SLIPPED THROUGH THE GATEWAY. ONLY, INSTEAD OF COMPLETING THE CYCLE, HE GOT REINCARNATED...

...INTO *YOU.*

BAM!

RU, *LISTEN* TO ME. WE CAN'T LET 'EM NEUTRALIZE YOU, GOT IT?

I KNEW THERE WAS SOMETHING ABOUT YOU FROM THE MOMENT WE MET. DIDN'T KNOW WHAT IT WAS, BUT I *KNEW* YOU WERE DIFFERENT.

BUT, HOW...?

YOU'RE A HECK OF A LOT MORE THAN A MISFIT, AND YOU AIN'T A NOBODY. YOU'RE SPECIAL. AND YOU GOT TO FIGHT FOR THAT, FOR *ALL* OF US!

FIGHT, KID! FIGHT WITH EVERYTHING YOU GOT!

RRRRRRR!

AND ME PARENTS SAID LEARNIN' TO *MAKE BOMBS* WAS A WASTE OF ME TIME.
FOOL TWATS.
ARK!
ARK!
ARK!
GOT A FEW DEVELOPMENTS TO CATCH YOU UP ON, VICKY...
LATER. WE HAVE TO GET TO JUNIE BEFORE SHE RUNS OUT OF TIME.

SILVER CITY

BEHIND THE SCENES

Issue 1
ENTACTUS (CASEY WULLNER)
Beehive Comic Collective Exclusive Variant Cover

THANK YOU

I would like to thank Luca Merli for lending his passion, brilliance and astonishing talent to this story. Christina Harrington for being the most reliable, trustworthy and creative editor a writer could ask for. Dave Sharpe for making my words sing. Mike Marts for everything he is every day. Jon and Lee Kramer for their endless support and for taking a chance on this title. Adam Glass for being a real Hollywood friend and for introducing me to comics. My favorite Brits, Nicole Rouyer Guillet and Daniel Broadhurst for lending authenticity to Victor's voice. My fabulous mama, Shari Cuartero, for proofreading every single script. Scott Dean, for loving this story so much. And, lastly, my forever puppy, Snax—thank you for loving me more than anyone deserves. I release you, sweet boy. Now, go help Ru save the world.

Olivia Cuartero-Briggs
August 2021

SILVER CITY™

In 2010, writer Olivia Cuartero-Briggs started writing SILVER CITY as a novel. She hand wrote the pages first—as seen here—in her journal.

Some excerpts from the first chapter are included on these pages:

"As Victor dug in his pocket, I noticed what looked like patches on the man's tan skin. Smoother than the skin of his face, but nearly the same color, each one appeared to be literally stitched on to him. A thread hung, broken, off a patch whose unfinished corner curled slightly off his cheek."

"The soul knows that the original body has passed, and those with an average to high mind-body connection will recognize the symptoms of death with no prior notion of what death is. It sounds extraordinary, but having experienced it, I can tell you that it's true."

"Did death mean that we could no longer feel? I was dead, I knew it, and yet I hadn't wept, screamed, raised my fists to the air raging against the injustice of a mere twenty-seven years in the world."

"There was an impact. I remember that, and then the vast dark of unconsciousness. Faint voices began to emerge, growing louder and more chaotic, the words indistinguishable until I woke with a start on the cool, wooden floor."

"'The Silver Knight isn't some stupid story,' Mick began, his black eyes now zeroed in on mine with intimidating intensity. 'He's the oldest soul.'"

"...as I walked to the railed edge, I could see a strange city sprawled out for miles. Mounting stacks of concrete and steel loomed over one another in cold succession as banners and illuminated signs jutted out over the narrow streets. High above the boxed towers, speared on a tall metal pole, a shining suit of armor pierced the static, grey sky, like a god keeping watch."

"Welcome to Silver City, the shithole of the afterlife."

me suited up and ready to go for training following week.

The next order of business was to get —d in the Silver City's obligatory Civic Program, or the S.C.C.D. Along with —get a job, pay bills and rent, the dream serves as our seeming Heaven, required —aonic obligatory volunteer work in order citizenship. Apparently, being shot in wasn't enough.

Still stoic, and requiring some coaxing Victor, we mounted the cold, courthouse-steps of the largest, oldest building in of Silver City, The University. This —s the same building in which I had landed —se two weeks ago, and seemed as the —me for all those entering our city of the dead.

"You missed your classes?" The professor eyed me with paternal scrutiny through wine-rimmed glasses. Seated across from me in a —white— loose white suit and nearly shoulder-length white hair, he was the closest resemblance to Jesus I had seen thusfar, however aged.

"No. I didn't know there were classes." In —life., though I was by no means a perfect exa— of civil humanity, I did try and play by the — Here, however, my whole pre-concieved notion —right, wrong, and have-to had shifted on a — axis. Late as I was, being told that I already acquired a Silver City tardy — about as insignificant as keeping track — time. My tone with the professor must h— expressed as much, but rather than a— anger or frustration, his eyes softened.

"It won't feel like this forever. You w— back to you, and when your feeling nothin— will find that our Silver City has j— much to offer you as the lands of the — I felt a slight twinge of sadness as —into his eyes, like the ~~glittering~~ hopeful spark— lighter's flint, and I realized tha— he was right.

Seated in the last row of the s— raked lecture hall, I could almos— see the very top of Samuel's head — he explained what Souls had — to know of the afterlife, and —

Dear Diary,

I lost control again. Or I think I did. I'm so hungry right now it's hard to know much of anything. Or maybe I'm just in denial. That's what Sticks says. That I'm in denial, I see things, and I need help. But I didn't just see that truck smash into the house, it was on the news. And if I had nothing to do with it, how come there was no driver? Parked trucks don't just move on their own. Not without me, anyway. And I'm pissed. Greg was an asshole. He didn't deserve what he got, but he wasn't a good person. But Miss Lila was. I liked her, and for once, I felt like a foster mom finally liked me. I wonder if she's worried about me? I wanted to call once I found Sticks, but I was afraid she'd ask where I was. I don't want to lie to her. I've lied to her too many times, and even though Sticks says I shouldn't say it, I killed her son. Doesn't matter if I meant to or not. Doesn't matter that he was a horrible person, or that he touched me, or that I said no. I killed him, and no amount of denial can change that. Damn it! I've been so good since the fire!

Sticks should be back soon. He went to get the rest of his stuff from Skid Row because I said I wouldn't stay there. That place is dangerous, and that's coming from a chick who accidentally pulled a cement truck into Miss Lila's living room. I found us a spot by the LA river in Studio City. It's nice enough. There are trees around and a gym nearby where we can shower. It's not the Ritz, wherever that is, but I have a tent, some clothes, and you, diary. So, I think I'll be okay until this blows over. Sticks said something about going north when have enough money for bus tickets. Said he has a cousin or something in Fresno, but I've never heard him mention him before.

I should go. Sticks will be back soon, and he doesn't like it when I write. Something about leaving a paper trail.

I hope he found some food.

Love,
Ru

I WOULD END THE WORLD FOR YOU

VICTOR SANKEY

YOU SAID THE WORLD WAS BROKEN
THAT NIGHT AT WORLD'S END WITH YOUR CREW
GOT PISSED AND SPARRED THE BARMAN
~~AND IN~~ THAT'S WHEN I BLOODY FELL FOR YOU.

YOU CALLED ME SCUM, A WASTE OF ~~SKIN~~ FLESH
WHEN I TRIED TO TAKE YOUR WINE
I HELD YOUR WRISTS YOU FLAILING MESS
THAT'S WHEN I FELT YOUR LIPS ON MINE.

~~AND~~ IT'S BLOODY STUPID, LOVE
BUT IT'S ALSO BLOODY TRUE
I WOULD END THE WORLD FOR YOU
I WOULD END THE WORLD FOR YOU

THE THIRTEENTH TIME YOU LEFT ME
FOR THAT GROTTY OLD COCK STAIN
I SWORE THAT I WAS DONE WITH YOU
AND CURSED YOUR BLOODY NAME

BUT WHEN YOU PHONED ME SOBBIN
I KNEW THAT VOW WAS FARCE
I STORMED HIS FLAT, SLAPPED HIS MUM
AND KICKED HIS PIGGY ARSE.

IT'S FECKIN BARMY, LOVE
BUT IT'S ALSO FECKIN TRUE
I WOULD END THE WORLD FOR YOU
I'D BLOODY END THIS WORLD FOR YOU

~~JUST ASK ME AND YOU'LL SEE IT TOO~~
DON'T BELIEVE ME, ASK ME TO
I'LL BLOODY END THIS WORLD FOR YOU.

SILVER CITY

artist sketchbook:
LUCA MERLI

issue #2 pg.12

issue #4 pg.17

RU CORRADO

VICTOR SANKEY

MICK BIANCHI AND SNAX

OLIVIA CUARTERO-BRIGGS writer
🐦 @OliviaCBriggs

Olivia Cuartero-Briggs is a native New Yorker, currently enjoying a career writing for television and comics in sunny Los Angeles. When she isn't scribbling away on her latest creation, she's hanging out with her awesome daughters, Quinn and Kit, and her husband, Scott who encourages her every day.

LUCA MERLI artist & colorist

Luca Merli was born in Tuscany, Italy. He attended the International School of Comics in Florence. He has worked with publishers like Casterman, Delcourt, Soleil and Glenat, dealing with both the inking and color, as well as with Disney Italy and Panini.

DAVE SHARPE letterer
🐦 @DaveLSharpe

Upon graduating from the Joe Kubert School in 1990, Dave went on to work at Marvel Comics as an in-house letterer, eventually running their lettering department in the late 90s and early 00s. Over the years, Dave has lettered hundreds of comics, such as *Spider-Girl*, *She-Hulk* and *The Defenders* for Marvel, and *Green Lantern*, *Harley Quinn*, and *Batgirl* for DC Comics. Dave now works on both *X-O Manowar* and *Faith* for Valiant Comics in addition to his lettering duties on several AfterShock titles.